the young singer

With Downloadable Piano Accompaniment

MP3 audio

MP3 download
carlfischer.com

Compiled and Edited by Richard D. Row

CONTENTS

CARL FISCHER®

RB82

ISBN 978-0-8258-1091-6

EDITOR'S FOREWORD

"THE YOUNG SINGER" is published in four volumes of Book One; SOPRANO: CONTRALTO or MEZZO-SOPRANO: TENOR: BARITONE or BASS. A few of the songs presented are common to all four of the volumes but generally speaking the contents of the four volumes are entirely different and contain songs composed for or suited to the specified voices.

"THE YOUNG SINGER" offers a varied and artistic list of songs in one cover quite different and apart from anything previously published. The songs are presented in the original language in which they were conceived and written.

For the benefit of those students who wish to sing certain of these songs in English, the Author has provided English texts which have proven to be singable as well as sensible! The stressed or high note always being on a singable vowel of such color as to maintain the intent of the composer in the original language. These English texts contain the basic poetic idea of the song while at the same time they are not the usual stodgy, inept and lifeless literal translations so often provided.

The editing has been carefully done in order to guide the singer as much as is possible (through the limitation of print) in the problems of interpretation and the original ideas of the inspired composer. Only the very basic fundamentals of interpretation can of necessity be found in the printed page — thus the final setting forth or re-creating of the Composers intent and purpose must come from the singer. Inspiration being a product of mind becomes one with the perfectly schooled body and through the coordination of these two factors a beautous outpouring of song is the result!

The Art of Singing is only acquired by patient, intelligent and systematic study — *always in accordance with the infallible Laws of Nature!* This book "The Young Singer" is not a method but a selection of songs which after much personal experience and research the Author has found to be the most valuable and useful for the young vocal student.

Richard H. Row

Morning Hymn

Morgen-Hymne
(Robert Reinick)

English version by
RICHARD D. ROW

GEORG HENSCHEL
Op. 46, No. 4.

So spake the Lord, His love be - stow - ing.
Da muss, was dun - kel ist, ver - ge - hen.

From heav'n a-bove   Filled with God's
Vom Him - mels-zelt   durch al - le

love   The an - gels soar in rap - ture
Welt   die En - gel freu - de - jauch - zend

glo - rious;   Sun - light oer all
flie - gen;   der Son - ne Strahl

Thy Beaming Eyes

W. H. GARDNER

EDWARD MacDOWELL
Op. 40, No. 3

With sentiment, passionately

When the Roses Bloom
Hoffnung

Louise Reichardt
(1778-1825)

Now Sleeps The Crimson Petal

TENNYSON.

ROGER QUILTER

Nebbie
Mists

ADA NEGRI
English text by
Richard D. Row

OTTORINO RESPIGHI

When Love Is Kind

THOMAS MOORE

Old English Melody
Arranged by A.L.

When Love is kind, cheer-ful and free

Love's sure to find well-come from me.

But when love brings heart-ache and pang,

But should I see Love giv'n to rove

To too or three, then good-bye Love!

Love must in short keep fond and true,

Thro' good re - port _____ and e - vil too.

f con anima

Else here I swear _____ young Love may go _____

For aught I _ care _____ to Je - ri - cho! Ah! _____

(laughing)

ha, ha, ha, to Je - ri - cho!

f staccato   *colla voce*   *f*   *ff*

✱ These four bars of Coda added by Miss Lehmann, can be omitted

A Swan
Ein Schwan

H. IBSEN
English version by
Richard D. Row

EDWARD GRIEG

Andante ben tenuto

My swan, my treas - ure, With
Mein Schwan, mein stil - ler, mit

snow - y white feath - er! Of thy songs sang me nev - er a sin - gle
wei - ssem Ge - fie - der! dei - ne won - ni - gen Lie - der ver - rieth kein

meas - ure! Slow - ly glid - ing in
Tril - ler! Ängst - lich sor - gend des

shad - ow - y bow - er, Sly, a - void - ing The
El - fen im Grun - de, glitt'st du hor - chend all -

For Music
Für Music

EMANUEL von GEIBEL
English text by Richard D. Row

ROBERT FRANZ
Op. 10, No. 1

Andante molto sostenuto

Eve-ning shad-ows fall-ing, Myr-iad stars a-light.
Nun die Schat-ten dun-keln, Stern an Stern er-wacht.

Sud-den-ly a long-ing Floods the air of night;
Welch ein Hauch der Sehn-sucht flu-tet durch die Nacht.

Through the sea of dream-ing Search-ing with-out rest,
Durch das Meer der Träu-me steu-ert oh-ne Ruh,

She Never Told Her Love

Shakespeare
(Twelfth Night)

JOSEF HAYDN

Who'll Buy My Lavender?

CARYL BATTERSBY, M. A.

EDWARD GERMAN

drives a - way Fret - ting moths of sil - ver grey. Who'll buy my

lav - en - der? La - dies fair, I pray that ye Like the lav - en -

der may be, And your fame, when you are gone,— Still in sweet - ness

lin - ger on Who'll buy? Who'll buy? Who'll buy? Who'll

Pleading
Bitte

NIKOLAUS LENAU
English text by
Richard D. Row

ROBERT FRANZ
Op. 9, No. 3

Look on me, O — eyes so ten - der, Let — me
Weil' auf mir, du — dunk - les Au - ge, ü - be

feel — thy won - drous — might. Ear - nest, mild, with — dream - y
dei - ne gan - ze — Macht, ern - ste, mil - de, — traü - me -

rap - ture, Fair as — day and dark as — night.
ri - sche, un - er - gründ - lich sü - sse — Nacht.

Morgen

To - Morrow

JOHN HENRY MACKAY
The English words by
Richard D. Row

RICHARD STRAUSS
Op. 27, No. 4

blau - en, wer-den wir still und lang-sam nie - der-stei - gen,
si - lent, your hand in mine. In dreams we'll slow-ly wan - der.

stumm___ wer-den wir uns in die Au - gen schau - en,
Mute,___ gaz-ing in each oth-er's eyes, en - rap - tured,

sempre più tranquillo

und auf uns sinkt des Glük - kes stum - mes Schwei -
On us fall - ing, a si - lent ben - e - dict -

gen.
ion.

Jesus, Jesus, Rest Your Head

American Folk Song
Arranged by
Richard D. Row

You have got a man - ger bed. Have you heard a -
bout our Je - sus, Have you heard a - bout His fate?
How His Moth - er went to the sta - ble On that Christ - mas
Eve so late? Winds were blow - ing, Cows were low - ing,

I'm Wearing Awa' To The Land O' The Leal

LADY NAIRN

ARTHUR FOOTE
Op. 13, No. 2

I've Been Roaming

CHARLES E. HORN

Andantino con anima

I've been roam-ing, I've been roam-ing, Where the mead-ow dew is sweet,— And I'm com-ing, and I'm com-ing, With its pearls up-on my feet; I've been

roam - ing, I've been roam - ing, Where the mead - ow dew is sweet, And I'm

com - ing, and I'm com - ing, With its pearls up - on my feet.

I've been roam - ing, I've been roam - ing, O'er the rose and lil - y fair, And I'm

com - ing, and I'm com - ing, With their blos - soms in my hair; I've been

roam - ing, I've been roam - ing, Where the mead - ow dew is sweet, And I'm

com - ing, and I'm com - ing, With its pearls up - on my feet.

p

I've been roam - ing I've been roam - ing Where the

ritard.

hon - ey - suck - le creeps, And I'm com - ing, and I'm com - ing, With its

Nymphs And Shepherds

The Libertine

HENRY PURCELL
*Accompaniment by
Myles B. Foster

THOMAS SHADWELL

Con moto

* Purcell only gives a Bass, unfigured, below the voice part.

Love Has Eyes

Sir HENRY BISHOP
Edited by Richard D. Row

Think On Me

Arranged by
Richard D. Row

Mary Queen of Scots
Alicia Ann Scott
(Lady John Scott)

Sapphic Ode
Sapphische Ode

HANS SCHMIDT
English text by
Richard D. Row

JOHANNES BRAHMS
Op. 94, No. 4

So thy kiss - es, sweet as the rose I cher - ish,
Auch der Küs - se Duft mich wie nie be - rück - te,

Kiss - es from thy lips like the flow'rs — red blos - som;
Die ich Nachts vom Strauch dei - ner Lip - pen pflück - te:
From thy
Doch auch

eyes with love — and deep e - mo - tion
dir, be - wegt im Ge - müth — gleich je - nen,
Tear — drops are
Thau — ten die

fall - - ing.
Thrä - - nen.

Songs My Mother Taught Me
Als Die Alte Mutter

English version by
Natalie MacFarren

ANTONIN DVOŘÁK
Op. 55, No. 4

On Wings Of Song
Auf Flügeln Des Gesanges

HEINRICH HEINE
English version by
Richard D. Row

F. MENDELSSOHN

A Pastoral

HENRY CAREY

Quickly

Flocks are sport - ing,
Flocks are bleat - ing,

Doves are court - ing War - bling lin - ets sweet - ly sing.
Rocks re - peat - ing, Val - leys e - cho back the sound.

Ah! _____ Ah! _____

Joy and plea - sure   With - out
Danc-ing, sing - ing,   Pip - ing,

mea - sure Kind - ly hail ___ the glo - rious spring,
spring - ing, Nought ___ but mirth ___ and joy ___ go round,

kind - ly hail ___ the ___ glo - rious spring.
nought but mirth ___ and joy ___ go round.

Ah! ___

Ah! ___

Ah! ___

Ah! ___

Sylvelin

English version by
Richard D. Row

CHRISTIAN SINDING

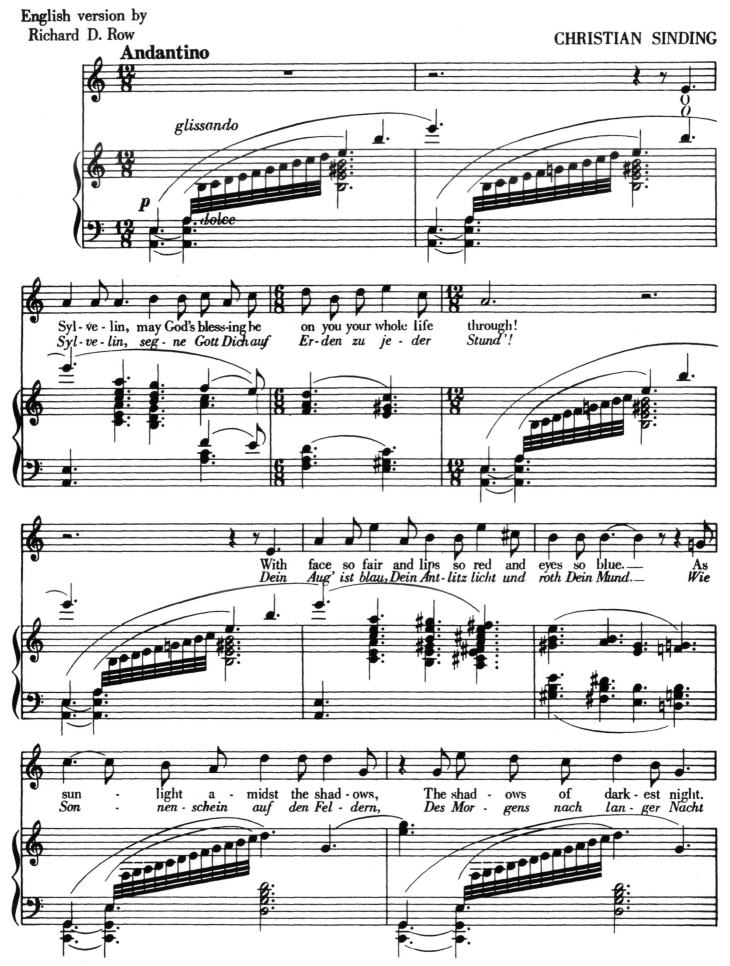

The Cuckoo

W. B. RANDS

LIZA LEHMANN

Moderato più tosto mosso

The Cuc - koo sat in the old pear - tree. "Cuc - koo!"_____ Rain - ing or snow - ing, nought cared he. "Cuc - koo!"_____

The Cuc-koo flew o-ver a house-top nigh

"Cuc-koo!" "Dear, are you at home, for

here am I?" "Cuc-koo!"

"I dare not o-pen the door to you, Cuc-

koo! _____ Per - haps you are not the

right Cuc - koo. Cuc - koo!" _____ "I

am the right Cuc - koo, the *pro - per* one; _____ Cuc - koo! _____ For

I am my fa - ther's on - ly son, Cuc-koo!"

a tempo
(frightened)

Primo tempo
Major

Primo tempo

pp a tempo

(proudly)

The Little Irish Girl

Words by
EDWARD TESCHEMACHER

Music by
HERMANN LÖHR

As I went out one eve - ning From Tip - per - a - ry Town, _ I

met a lit - tle Col - leen A - mong the heath - er brown; "Ah!" says

I "Per-haps you're lone - ly" She tossed her pret-ty curl, "Well

may- be I pre-fer it!" Och! the dear lit - tle girl!

Says

I "Per- haps you're mar - ried?" Says she, "Per- haps I'm not!" Says

Passing By

EDWARD PURCELL
Piano Accompaniment
by Richard D. Row

a little more moving

Her ges-ture, mo - tion and her smile Her wit, her voice my heart ____ be - guile, Be - guile my heart, I know not why, And yet I love her 'till I die.

* If the singer cannot sing this entire phrase on one breath, take a catch breath after the word "country."

SACRED VOCAL COLLECTIONS

FREDRICKSON

CHURCH SOLOISTS FAVORITES
RB65 HIGH RB66 LOW

SACRED DUET MASTERPIECES
RB58 BOOK 1—HIGH & LOW
RB59 BOOK 2—MED. & LOW
RB60 BOOK 3—TWO HIGH VOICES

SACRED SONG MASTERPIECES
BOOK 1 RB49 HIGH RB50 LOW
BOOK 2 RB75 HIGH RB76 LOW

SACRED SONGS FOR ALL OCCASIONS
RB61 HIGH RB62 LOW

HARRELL

SACRED HOUR OF SONG
O2933 HIGH O2893 MED

ROW

SOLOISTS PRACTICAL LIBRARY OF SACRED SONGS
BOOK 1
RB47 HIGH
RB48 LOW
BOOK 2
RB73 HIGH
RB74 LOW

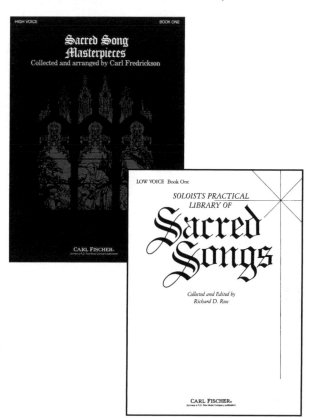

THE FRED BOCK AND PAUL JOHNSON COLLECTIONS OF CONTEMPORARY AND INSPIRATIONAL FAVORITES

HOW MAJESTIC IS YOUR NAME
CAT. NO. SGB501

FOR THE SAKE OF THE CALL
CAT. NO. SGB505

THE MAJESTY AND GLORY OF YOUR NAME-
CAT. NO. SGB506

Enjoy these Innovative and Unique Vocal Collections
- Great Repertoire
- Recital Material
- For the Serious Voice Student!

Daron Aric Hagen Songbook

No composer of the present generation has contributed more song repertoire or received more favorable attention for his vocal writing than Daron Aric Hagen. The Daron Aric Hagen Songbook collects 60 songs, and includes the complete cycles *Larkin Songs* (2000) (to poems of English poet Philip Larkin), *Phantoms of Myself* (2000) (devoted to poems of Susan Griffin), *Muldoon Songs* (1989) (to poems of Pulitzer Prize winning poet, Paul Muldoon), *Figments* (2000) (set to poems of Alice Wirth Gray) and three anthology cycles; *Letting Go* (2002), *Love in a Life* (1981-1999), and *The Heart of a Stranger* (1983-1999). The Songbook also includes a foreword by tenor Paul Sperry, introduction by Dr. Carrie deLapp Culver, a bibliography of related publications by and about Daron Hagen and a list of recordings of his vocal music. Great for those interested in serious vocal literature!

VF3 – Book – (ISBN 0-8258-4916-0)

DARON ARIC
HAGEN
SONGBOOK

CARL FISCHER®

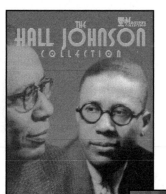

The Hall Johnson Collection
for Voice and Piano (with 2 CDs)

An inspiring compilation of Hall Johnson's beautiful settings of traditional African-American spirituals and original songs (some set to the poems of Langston Hughes), this collection includes a full recording of the complete works with introductory essays by noted authorities John Motley, Julius Williams, and Dr. Eugene Thamon Simpson.

VF5 – Book with 2 CDs – (ISBN 0-8258-4964-0)

Lily Pons Song Album
Selected Coloratura Repertoire
for High Voice and Piano
Edited by Frank La Forge

This one volume compilation contains concert pieces and arias of the legendary coloratura soprano Lily Pons (1898-1976) from the original archives of Frank La Forge. The collection includes the music of Mozart, Rossini, Debussy, Fauré, Handel and Grétry and others.

VF2 – Book – (ISBN 0-8258-4706-0)

John Duke Collection
Richard Cory and
Selected Songs for Voice and Piano
Compiled by Paul Sperry

Included in this handsome volume are some of John Duke's finest songs featuring his three celebrated setting of poems by Edward Arlington Robinson (Richard Cory, Miniver Cheevy and Luke Havergal).

VF1 – Book – (ISBN 0-8258-4229-8)